A Safe Place to Land

Written by Lisa Thompson
Pictures by Craig Smith

The pirates were looking for a safe place to land.

"Pirates can't land here," said the Captain.

The pirates sailed on.

"This is Mermaid Rock," said Fingers, the parrot.
"We can't land here."

The pirates sailed past a sleeping sea monster.

"This is not a safe place to land," said Lizzie.

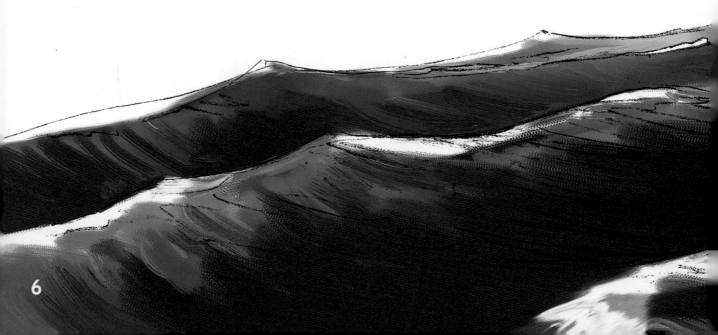

The pirates sailed on and on.

They saw a shipwreck.

"This is not a safe place," said the Cook.

The pirates stopped by a little island.

"Woof! Woof! No food here!"
said Bones, the sea dog.

The pirates sailed past Skull Rock.

"We don't want to stop here!"
said all the pirates.

Then the pirates sailed into Pirate Cove.

"This is the perfect place for a pirate," said the Captain.